© 1994 Geddes & Grosset Ltd
Published by Geddes & Grosset Ltd,
New Lanark, Scotland.

ISBN 1 85534 587 0

Printed and bound in Slovenia.

Dick Whittington

Retold by Judy Hamilton
Illustrated by R. James Binnie

Tarantula Books

Once upon a time, in a small country village in England, there lived a boy called Dick Whittington. His parents were both dead and he had no other family. The people of the village were kind and gave him odd jobs to do, but he was very poor. He felt sure that he could make a better life for himself.

One day, a roving band of musicians came to the village. They played all day in the village square, then when evening came, they packed up their instruments and prepared to move on. Dick asked them where they were going next.

"We're going to London," they told him, "to make our fortune. They say that the streets are paved with gold!"

That night as Dick slept, he dreamt he was walking on golden pavements.

Next day, Dick got up early, packed up what few possessions he had in a large cloth, and set off in the same direction as that in which the band had gone the night before. He had never been far from the village before, and London was a long way away. Dick walked without stopping until after midday, when he stopped by a stream to take a drink. Then he carried on walking. He had no food and his feet were beginning to hurt. By late afternoon his legs and feet were aching and he was very tired. Just then a man in a cart pulled up and kindly offered him a ride to London. Dick thanked the man and got into the back of the cart. They bumped along for many miles more and it was well after dark when they reached the city.

Dick curled up in an alley-way and went to sleep. When he awoke, the noise of the city was like music to his ears. But he could see that the paving stones in the streets around him were quite ordinary.
He had to find the streets that were paved with gold and make his fortune.

Dick searched all day in vain. Nobody whom he asked had heard of streets paved with gold. He was very tired and hungry. As the day wore on, he began to look for work, to earn enough for some food and a bed for the night. But everybody was too busy to listen to him.

Exhausted and disappointed, Dick huddled in the doorway of a huge house and went to sleep.

He was woken the next morning by a kindly voice

"You look worn out, my lad. Have you nowhere to go?

Dick looked up and saw a well-dressed man smiling down at him.

"I have come to London to make my fortune," explained Dick. "I heard the streets were paved with gold."

"I am afraid you will never find golden streets. You have to work hard to make your fortune in this life," the man told him gently. "But you can work in my kitchen. Come inside and get some food. I'll tell the Cook to show you what to do and find you a bed in the servant quarters."

Dick's new master was a wealthy merchant who owned ships which sailed the world. The work was very hard, but his master was kindly, and his pretty young daughter always had a friendly word for Dick.

Then the day came when the merchant had to sail overseas. Life became much harder for poor young Dick. The other servants in the house began to bully him. The cook was especially unkind to him, and would beat him for the smallest mistakes. Dick's only friend in the house was the merchant's daughter but he rarely saw her, for the cook kept him so hard at work, from dawn until late at night, that he hardly ever left the kitchens. To make things worse, a family of mice had nested in his tiny room. The noise of the mice kept him awake all night.

Early one morning, bruised and tired, Dick made up his mind to run away.

Packing together his clothes and what little money he had, Dick crept out of the house before anyone else was awake, heading out of the city. It was still dark and very cold. Dick was determined to leave, so he bravely marched on. But then something happened which changed his mind. Just as he reached the edge of the city, the bells of London began to ring. Dick stopped to listen.

"Turn again Whittington, thrice mayor of London" the bells seemed to be saying. Dick listened and again the bells rang out, with the same message. Dick turned back along the road. Three times mayor of London! Could this be true?

He had to hurry to get back before everybody woke up and realised that he was missing.

On his way back to the merchant's house, Dick passed through the early morning market. He met woman selling kittens beside one of the stalls. Dic took out all the money he had. It wasn't enough, but the woman felt sorry for him and let him buy one of her kittens.

Dick tucked it inside his shirt and hurried back to the merchant's house.

The kitten grew fast, and became Dick's constan companion. It chased the mice from Dick's room, and he slept at night once more. The other servant still bullied him, but now he had his cat as a friend The merchant's daughter played with it while Dic was working.

"You have a fine friend there, Dick," she said to him one day, and Dick knew it was true.

One day the merchant gathered all his servants together. He was setting out on a very long trip. He wanted to give all the servants the chance of sending something to sell in the country to which he was going. Everybody found something to sell; the gardener had tools which he had made, the cook had some jars of pickled fruit, the housekeeper had a tapestry which she had sewn. But Dick had nothing to sell. He had no possessions. Then the merchant's daughter suggested that he send his cat. The merchant agreed, for the cat would be useful catching mice on board ship. Dick felt very sad, but gave up his cat to sell. He gave the cat one last hug and said goodbye. The merchant packed all the servants' goods into his carriage and set off for the harbour where his ship was waiting.

Poor Dick felt terribly lonely without his cat. The cook was becoming more cruel and working him harder every day. The mice came back to his room and kept him awake. Dick was miserable. Once again, he tried to run away from the merchant's house, but once again the sound of the bells stopped him.

"Turn again Whittington, thrice mayor of London."

So Dick stayed, and the only thing that cheered his life was the smile of the merchant's daughter.

Dick might have felt better if he had known what was happening to his cat far across the sea. The ship had been at sea for several weeks when it came to land at last in a distant country. Hearing of a strange ship in the harbour, the king invited the merchant to the palace.

Dick could not believe his ears when the merchant got back to London. His cat had been precious to him as a friend, and now it was precious to someone else.

The cook and the servants were outraged when they saw the treasures which the king had paid for Dick's cat. But there was nothing they could do.

"You have made your fortune, Dick." said the merchant's daughter. "You can now become a merchant in your own right."

Dick's days in the kitchen were over. He left the merchant's house the next day and bought himself a fine mansion. Then he bought a beautiful ship of his own and hired a crew. He was ready to start trading overseas in distant lands.

The king held a great feast at the palace for the merchant and his crew. The merchant sold many of the things he had brought with him. Then he noticed a lot of rats scuttling around the floors of the palace. One rat climbed onto the table and stole some of the food. The king told the merchant that they had tried every kind of poison and potion, but nothing would get rid of the rats. The merchant told the king about Dick's cat. So the king, who had never seen a cat before, asked to see it. The cat was brought into the palace and right away, it began to catch the rats, one by one. The king was astounded to see such a clever creature. He gave the merchant a chest full of treasure in payment for it.

The merchant set sail to return to London.

The years passed and Dick's wealth grew. He owned several ships which travelled all over the world. He became a good friend of the merchant who had shown such kindness to him. In time, he fell in love with the merchant's daughter and asked her to marry him. They had many happy years together. Dick became a respected man in London, and was filled with pride when he was asked to become Lord Mayor.

The bells of London had been right, for after that he became Lord Mayor of London two more times. "Turn again Whittington, thrice Mayor of London!" But no matter what happened, Dick never forgot his precious cat. Before any of his ships set sail, Dick always made sure that there was a marmalade cat on board.

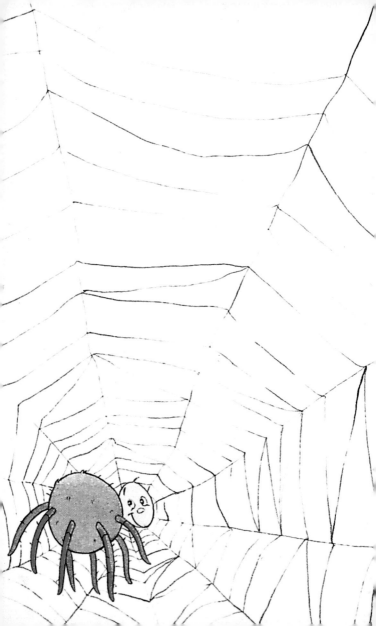